# ADVENTURES OF

# RICHARD WAGNER

# ADVENTURES OF
# RICHARD WAGNER

*By*

*OPAL WHEELER*

*ILLUSTRATED BY FLOYD WEBB*

---

*E P. DUTTON & COMPANY, INC*
*New York, 1960*

LIBRARY OF CONGRESS CATALOG CARD NUMBER: 60–6016

*For*

BETH

# ADVENTURES OF
# RICHARD WAGNER

# CHAPTER ONE

BOOM. BOOM. BOOM.—BANG—BOOM—ZING!

The people in the Dresden theatre sat up, startled. Who would dream of pounding on the bass drums right in the middle of the play? Not a single word could anyone hear, and waves of angry buzzing darted from row to row.

"What a frightful noise! Dreadful! An evil monster at work somewhere!"

The poor actors on the stage could not believe their ears. How would anyone dare to play such a trick in the largest hall of the great city?

Ludwig Geyer shouted his lines above the din and strode from the platform, a stern gleam in his eyes. Frantically he darted through the dressing rooms, calling as he searched:

"Dicker! Dicker! Come out, I say!"

He came upon the small drummer suddenly. In a far corner of the storeroom under the stage, four-year-old Richard stood on a low box, his blue eyes glowing like stars. A stout stick was in each hand as he beat with all his strength on the giant drums, ending with a ringing crash on the golden cymbals.

BANG. BOOM. ZING!

"Dicker!"

The short arms stopped in mid-air and bright laughter pealed through the dim room.

"Listen, father! I can play almost as loud as old Nels!"

Ludwig seized the sticks and swept the drummer boy from the stand.

"Enough! You have ruined the play with your pounding!" he cried. "Look—the audience is leaving the theatre. What a horrible day for us all!"

Two curious blue eyes were glued to the peep-hole. It was true. Long lines of people were moving through the aisles to the doors. But more terrible by far were the solemn words over the fair head.

"No playhouse for you for many a day, young man!"

The punishment was greater than he could bear.

14

Choking sobs filled his throat as Richard followed the tall figure through the darkening, snowy streets of Dresden.

No more bright lights and music and dancing? No trunks to explore, with wigs and funny shoes and strange masks that made chills of fright scamper up his spine? No romping with the actors and sitting in the orchestra pit with the men?

But above all, he would not be with his actor stepfather, whom he loved more than anyone in the whole world.

"Playhouse tomorrow?" The small voice behind the lean figure never stopped its pleading.

"NO playhouse!" The final answer cut still deeper into the heart of the weeping drummer boy.

15

Mother Geyer looked anxiously at her young son as through the dinner, even with the coaxing of his older brothers and sisters, no food would he touch.

"Come, small one. Bed is the only place to end such a dreadful day as this."

Ludwig swung the little figure to his shoulder and followed Mother Geyer's flickering candle up the narrow stairway.

Tucked under warm blankets, Richard's troubles were ended at last, and as the blue eyes closed, Ludwig turned anxiously to his companion.

"Strange Hannah, that the will of this child is so strong," he mused. "You do not think that I have been too harsh with the lad?"

He felt a hand slip into his own.

"Ah no, my dear. A kind and patient father you have been, since you came into our home two short years ago. The children could not love you more. Nor I."

Ludwig's arm encircled the slender shoulders and together they looked back at the sleeping child.

"A little secret just for your ears, good wife. Of all the children, this is the one nearest my heart. I feel a star rising in this boy. Where it will lead him I know not. Ah, Hannah, what a bright, stirring spirit is here."

The days were long, indeed, for young Richard as he sat at the window for hours, watching for his father to return from the theatre.

At the first sight of the jaunty figure swinging through the pale shadows, he sprang through the doorway to throw himself into the outstretched arms. Laughing and crying in the same breath, he rode on the strong shoulders, chattering like a magpie.

"Did the actors miss me, father? And the people clapped hard today? And did they find the right costume with the red wig for big Hans?"

Ludwig smiled as he swept the eager figure to the floor.

"Softly, Dicker, softly. And yes to all of your questioning." He patted the fair head. "Now a big surprise for a patient little dormouse. We rehearse a new play tomorrow, and you will have a part all your own."

The news was almost too good to be true. With a shout, Richard wheeled around the room in dizzy circles.

"A big part like yours, father?"

"Ah no, little one. You will be an angel in shining new costume. It is a good play, and I hope the king will be well pleased."

On the night of the performance the young angel stood ready behind the curtain in pure white costume, his snowy wings brushing the floor. Ludwig, handsome in scarlet cape, was close at his side.

"Remember, Dicker, not to move about. You must stand as still as a stone, and then walk quietly from the stage after my long speech."

Richard looked anxiously into the face above him.

"But how will the king notice me if I am so quiet?"

"He will see you, small one, never fear."

Suddenly the warning bell sounded.

"Everyone in place! Curtain going up!"

Richard's heart beat fast as he watched the giant mass of crimson velvet rise slowly to the rafters.

Suddenly a hand clutched his shoulder.

"It is time, Dicker. Walk slowly to the chalk circle and stand very still," commanded Ludwig.

The small white figure stepped onto the great stage, and at the sea of faces smiling up at him, an idea popped into his mind. An angel should take a little flight before settling down to earth.

Grasping the stick at his back, he worked it up and down. The long wings flapped nicely. Faster and faster he moved the rod and began to run in a wide circle.

Waves of laughter swept through the audience and Richard grinned with delight. Surely the king

was looking at him now! Around and around the stage he ran as fast as his short legs would carry him, snowy robe whipping against his knees.

Suddenly, as he steered himself toward the white mark, the wings broke loose and fell to the stage with loud clatter.

Peals of merriment rolled over the audience as solemnly the small angel clutched them in his arms and strode manfully to his place in the chalk circle.

In his place of honor, the King of Saxony shook with laughter and nodded toward the stage.

"The small one there—who is he?" he chuckled. "Never have I known an angel to speak so loud without uttering a single word."

The very next day, what should arrive at the theatre from the Saxon ruler but the most beautiful, giant cake, with rows of delicately iced flowers.

Richard nodded happily as he sampled the icing.

"It's because the king liked my part so well," he declared, lifting off a rose and a lily and popping them into his mouth.

With the help of his father and a sword, he cut slices for everyone, until there was nothing left of the beautiful cake but one last piece in his hand.

"For Cäcilie," he announced solemnly, carrying it home with great pride.

Next to his father he loved his small sister more than anyone else, and as she grew older the two were constant companions. Contentedly she followed him like a shadow out to the tiny rabbit hut, to listen to the endless stories that came from his lips, though very little did she understand.

"Now we will make a play, just like the theatre," he announced one morning. "You will be the pure white dove, floating on a silvery pond, and a fierce tiger is hiding in the bushes, waiting to eat you alive."

Swiftly he took off her white pinafore.

"Now you must look like a snowy dove," he explained, tying it securely over her head.

Suddenly blinded, the small bird began to whimper, but was silenced by the thundering voice in her ears:

"Be still, or the hungry tiger will finish you off in a few mouthfuls!"

Richard's eyes lighted on a large wooden tub, half filled with the night's rainfall. Just the thing—a wonderful pond for the snow-white bird.

Groaning with his burden, he lifted her to the iron rim, and with a big shove pushed her into the chill water.

"Swim, little bird," he called. "Swim nicely, my dear white dove."

Poor Cäcilie! Sputtering and screaming and gasping for breath, her shrill cries brought Mother Hannah running from the house.

"My baby! Oh, my poor little lamb! What will that child do next?" she cried, untying the struggling bird.

Late that evening Ludwig listened soberly to the morning's adventure. There was no doubt of it. The child's mind was too full of the theatre.

"It is time to teach the boy, and tomorrow I will take him under my wing," said he. "Perhaps a few lessons in painting will tell if he might be an artist someday."

The next morning was fresh and clear, with puff-ball clouds rolling high overhead. Richard, happy as a lark, swung the small pack over his shoulder like his hero father, and after a ride into the country, struck off over the fields.

"Never a better day for painting, eh, Dicker? But remember, lad, one must be very patient indeed, to become a good artist."

Choosing a spot near a clump of scraggly oaks, Ludwig carefully set up the easels. Himself a painter of portraits as well as an actor, he placed the half-finished likeness of the king before him. With a few tacks, a fresh sheet of paper covered the small board at his side.

"Now you will surprise me with a splendid picture of trees and billowing clouds," said he. "Use the chalks lightly, child, and see if you can match the glorious colors around you."

With a loving pat on the fair head, Ludwig turned to his easel and was lost in his work. The young artist was safely beside him, his heart beating rapidly under his short green jacket as he hummed a merry tune and set about the business at hand.

Suddenly a baby squirrel scuttled through the grass at his feet and was off to the brow of the hill. Throwing the chalk over his shoulder, Richard was after him, heels flying. But alas, the small furry creature darted neatly into a hollow log and was lost from sight.

With a sigh Richard sat swinging his short legs, waiting for his new friend to appear. He would capture it and take it home to Cäcilie. What fun it

would be to train it and teach it tricks. Then all the world would come and watch the wonder animal.

But the waiting was too long, and with a bound Richard was off again, seeking fresh adventure.

Far above his head a bird in a tree called sharply. There was sure to be a whole nest of her soft, downy babies hidden among the leaves, thought the young explorer.

His shoes were off in a trice and he began to climb. Higher and still higher he followed the shrill whistle, keeping a sharp lookout for the nest.

There—what was that brown pocket at the end of the slender branch? It must be the home of the birds!

"Dick-er! Dick-er!" The call floated far over the sunny field as Ludwig searched for the runaway painter.

Suddenly his breath caught in his throat as his eyes lighted on a small, dangling figure, swinging and swaying high in the tree.

"Child! Child!" he gasped, running at top speed over the meadow. "Oh, he will surely fall! What will his poor mother say? Poor, dear Hannah!"

Out of breath, he reached the tree.

"Hold tight, boy, and do not be frightened," he called in quavering tones. "I will get help quickly!"

He was off again and before long was racing back, a farmer with a ladder close behind. Fearfully he looked up into the spreading branches.

"Why—where is the child?" he cried in alarm.

A terrible thought sprang into his mind. The little one must have fallen and someone had carried him home.

"What a day! What a dreadful day for his mother!" he mourned, tears stinging his eyelids.

At his side, the farmer was carefully scanning the field. Suddenly his keen eyes lighted as he pointed a bony finger toward the far western end.

"Look you, sir—is that the boy down yonder?"

Ludwig shielded his eyes from the sun and clapped the man on the shoulder.

"Yes! Yes! That is the lad!" His joy could scarcely be contained and his voice was not too steady as he added, "God be thanked for the miracle of this day."

In a short time they were back at the easels, to find the small painter blithely at work. His face was smudged with red chalk, and in bold letters he was signing his name at the bottom of the paper.

"Dicker! How did you ever get down from the tree?"

With a bright nod, the young artist looked up into the frightened eyes.

"It was too long to wait, so I just dropped," he explained simply. Waving a hand at his easel, he declared with pride, "See, it is finished—the King of Saxony."

Back in Dresden, Mother Geyer smiled at the ruler with strange green eyes and a crooked blue mouth wandering to yellow ears.

"The poor king would hardly recognize himself," she chuckled. "Perhaps the child would do better with music, Ludwig."

A few mornings later, after his older sisters had finished their lessons at the piano with the best teacher in all Dresden, Richard took his place at the keyboard, a scowl knitting his brow.

"A brave new pupil," the tall woman beamed. "And so eager to learn on the very first day."

But the young scholar was already at work, pumping the pedals up and down to hear them squeak.

"Ah, no, my dear. The feet we use much later.

Come now, we will play a little scale. So. . . ."

Richard watched for a moment, his short fingers pressed firmly against the keys until he could bear it no longer. He pushed the big hand away and looked up into the solemn face.

"Listen, Frau Hübsch. I can make a big noise like a storm."

Standing on the loud pedal, he banged his elbows on the low keys with a great crash. At the look of horror on the stern face above, Richard laughed gaily.

"Child! Child! The piano is groaning at such terrible sounds," cried the teacher. "Quickly—let us go back to the lovely little scale again."

Through the days the new scholar would not go near the keyboard, even with the coaxing of his sisters, who played very well indeed.

"I will learn pieces by myself," he declared stoutly, "when I get a little time to think about them."

To the surprise of everyone in the household, he started one morning, carefully picking out little tunes that he so often heard. Very hard he worked until he could play them without stumbling.

31

Well content with his performance, the young music maker slid down from the chair.

"Now I can play the piano, so I won't need lessons with Frau Hübsch," he decided.

His mother sighed.

"Ah well, perhaps it is better to wait until you are older, child." She patted the fair head. "And now an errand will keep you from mischief for a time. Run to the grocer for onions and cheese, Dicker. And mind—no forgetting this time!"

He was gone with a shout and soon found his friend, Herr Klepperbein, tying up bundles near the musty bins, the tassel on his cap bobbing merrily.

"Good day little grasshopper," he called. "Just help yourself to a raisin or two, and I'll be with you before you can jump at a fly."

32

Raisins! Richard scurried to the groaning box in the corner and his hands dug deep into the sticky mass. When his mouth and pockets were filled to overflowing, shuffling footsteps sounded behind him.

"So—and now what would your good mother want this day, I wonder?" Herr Klepperbein bent his knees to search the bright face.

Richard stopped chewing for a moment, lost in thought. But try as he would, he could not remember.

"Cutlets perhaps?" the rumbling voice suggested. "Won't do a mite of harm to send along a packet. Come in right handy, with so many mouths to feed."

The large bundle safely in his arms, Dicker arrived at his door, to be met by Mother Hannah.

"Meat again!" She threw up her hands in despair. "And not a sign of onions or cheese."

The young messenger had already skipped away to divide his treasure with Cäcilie. But the good odor of sizzling cutlets sent him flying back to the kitchen. Sniffing hungrily, he hovered over the iron skillet, watching his favorite meat browning and spitting merrily over the red coals.

Suddenly a loud knocking sent Mother Hannah to the door. As quick as a wink, the long fork was in Richard's hand and plop! went the cutlets onto the dripping board.

Now for some quick bites. Each piece was hastily sampled, and the last and fattest of the lot thrust into his trouser pocket. Oh, how it burned! Gasping with pain, Richard hobbled toward the wide cupboard just as his mother reached the stove.

"My cutlets! How—where—" she cried in astonishment. "We are bewitched! My cutlets have disappeared into thin air!"

Suddenly she spied the small figure slipping painfully behind the cabinet door. So—there was the culprit!

Mother Hannah shook her head. Did the child need meat so badly, then? Only a few nights ago a dog had slipped into the kitchen and made off with Richard's bone. With a shout he was after him and down through the town they raced, right under a startled horse. The frightened animal had kicked violently, the blow landing on Richard's chest. A man had carried the weeping boy home and an anxious time there was, indeed, for a whole night and a day.

"Punishment enough, without more," sighed Mother Hannah, bringing out a fresh supply of meat. And not much time for cooking, with guests arriving at any moment.

Richard loved the jolly evenings in his home, when the good friends of Dresden gathered together in the large living room to sing and play on instruments. Sometimes there were wonderful puppet shows and plays for the guests to act, all written by father Geyer.

But tonight the evening began in a different way when Ludwig clapped his hands and called:

"Cossack! Where is my little Cossack acrobat?"

Scarcely were the words out of his mouth when

into the middle of the room leaped Richard, turning cart wheels, spinning in dizzy circles, standing on his head while his father counted slowly to ten, and ending with a frenzied Russian dance.

There was loud applause and cries of "Bravo, little Cossack!"

Richard was proud to be a part of the entertainment. But when it was time for music, he sat as still as a mouse in his favorite nook near the hearth, drinking in the glorious sounds.

Ludwig took his place at the piano to sing and the young listener clapped and cheered lustily, his face wreathed in smiles. Like a shadow he crept to his father's feet as the beautiful voice filled the room, to sit entranced until the last mellow note had died away.

But the moment the tones of the violin reached his ears, he raced from the room and hid in a far corner of the house. There, his head buried under a pillow, he shivered and shook until the sounds were ended.

His older sister, Rosalie, already a fine singer in the theatre, followed him quietly. Bending over her small brother, she spoke to him softly.

"Tell me, little Dicker, why do you run away from the violin music?"

Still trembling, and his cheeks washed with tears, Richard slowly turned his face to the light.

"It hurts me here—and here," he whispered, pointing to his chest and ears. "Oh, Rosalie, it hurts me because it is too beautiful!"

Back to the theatre he went happily with **Lud-wig**, and his heart was filled to overflowing when at last he was allowed to play small parts now and then. But his mother was sorely troubled.

"We must never allow this child to become an actor," she declared firmly. "There is plenty for him to learn outside of the theatre."

One morning Richard was awakened by the early sun smiling down at him from the high nursery window. Pulling his short woolen shirt over his head, he skipped into the warm kitchen and stopped short in surprise.

There was Mother Hannah, busily folding his clothes and packing them neatly in a small wicker basket.

"You go on a little journey today, my son," she explained with a brave smile, stopping to fill his blue bowl with steaming porridge. "A boy of six should begin real lessons."

"And Cäcilie will go, too?"

"Ah no, my child. The school is just for boys. And lucky that Vicar Wetzel has agreed to take you into his house with other young pupils."

Hannah looked into the eager, questioning face and her arms closed around him in a warm hug. A lump filled her throat at the thought of sending this child of her heart away from his home so early.

"Dear little Dicker, you will try hard to learn all that the master tells you," said she, wiping the small face clean. "Then when you come home again, what wonderful tales you will have to tell us."

Buttoned into his best Sunday jacket, Richard felt very important as he stood clutching his wicker basket. Soon rolling wheels sounded on the roadway, and in a flurry of excitement he climbed gaily into the carriage with Ludwig, and waved a last farewell to those who loved him so dearly.

"In a little while I will come back for you, Cäcilie," he called, leaning from the window.

With a shout from the driver they were on their way, rumbling over the cobbled streets that led to the country highway, and adventure in the small village of Possendorf.

# CHAPTER TWO

Richard felt like a mighty explorer, off to strange lands at the end of the world. He bounced on the carriage seat and twisting and turning, peered through the small panes.

On the edge of the city, he watched with bated breath as a thin slip of a chimney sweep scrambled to the very top of a roof, to begin the grimy work of the day.

Quaint villages and farmhouses slipped by, with sturdy hands on the way to warm kitchens with foaming pails of milk.

"Whoa! Whoa!" As the coach came to a sudden halt, Richard laughed heartily at the squealing litter of pigs milling over the roadway. In a dither, a poor man in patched jacket was darting at them with a long stick.

"Hyah, hyah, hyah! Git along there, you ornery critters!" he shouted. "Market still a long way off, and miles to travel!"

The carriage had not gone on very far, when a shaggy dog barking at the wheels sent Richard flying to the door.

"I'll just wrap him in my coat to get warm," he called.

Ludwig grasped the eager arm just in time.

"Better let him find his way home, Dicker. His master would be too lonely without him."

"Possendorf Village. Two out!" called the driver at last, pulling on the brakes until they screeched and whined.

Richard looked curiously at the low rambling house of Vicar Wetzel, hugging the side of the road like a giant tortoise.

At Ludwig's knock, the door opened in a magical way and in went the new pupil, tugging his wicker basket after him. There, holding out a big hand in welcome, was the director in solemn black coat.

"An eager, bright boy, if ever I saw one," he declared warmly, bending his knees to look closely at the newcomer. "Will you have us call you by your real name, Richard Wagner, or by your stepfather's?"

The young pupil looked into the kind, wrinkled face, puzzled for a moment.

"But I have only one father now, so I'd better be Richard Geyer," he answered thoughtfully. "Besides, he's the best man in the whole world, and he's a great actor in the theatre, and someday—"

He paused suddenly, an eerie feeling creeping over him as he reached for the strong, comforting handclasp of his hero. But Ludwig had slipped quietly away, his heart heavy within him at leaving behind the child so dear to him.

For the first time in his six years, Richard was alone, far from his own home. Waves of fear swept over him, and running to the door, he shouted with all his might:

"Father! Father! I'm coming—Wait for me!"

But only the schoolmaster's words sounded in his ears, and a strange hand was on his shoulder.

"Did you know that our dog had puppies just two days ago? She hid from us, Richard, and we hunted and hunted until the crying of the little ones led us to her." The deep, mellow voice rambled on. "Would

you like to have a look at the new family with me?"

Brushing his eyes with his coat sleeve, Richard swallowed his tears.

"Oh—oh yes, sir!"

He looked up into the warm smile and slipped his hand into the big one dangling at his side. Cautiously the two felt their way down the dark stairs to a musty coal cellar. There, in a broken washtub lined with a tattered coat, were four soft brown puppies, sound asleep against their mother.

Richard cried out with delight, reaching eagerly for the tiny creatures.

"Sh! Better not waken them now, lad, or we may have a little trouble with their mother. We'll visit them a bit later, yes?"

Up the stairs they crept and suddenly came upon

a scrambling heap of boys at the end of a hallway. Shouting and laughing, they struggled over a giant red ball.

"Attention!" The master blew a shrill blast on his whistle, and at once the students raced to the tall figure, climbing over him with shrieks of joy.

"Steady, lads, steady!" the calm voice warned. "There is a tasty surprise awaiting us below. I hope you will be hungry enough to enjoy it, young gentlemen."

There were squeals of delight as hungry students fell upon the steaming platefuls of the good food, dished out by motherly Frau Wetzel. In no time at all not a single mouthful was left.

"Time for stories upstairs, everyone." The command brought ringing cheers.

Richard ran to the vicar's side, his face alight.

"Stories!" he cried in shrill tones. "Why, this is a good school. I think I'll stay awhile!"

He sat without moving, his eyes glued to the master's face as he listened to the exciting adventures of Robinson Crusoe and the life story of the great composer, Mozart.

There were lessons as well, and the hours passed quickly. Almost before he knew it, Dicker was in his narrow iron cot, drifting far away into the blissful world of slumber.

The vicar smiled as he left the quiet line of boys and tiptoed to the warm room beyond.

"All is well," he announced to his cheery little wife, who sat in a pool of light, busily mending torn jackets and trousers. "The new little one shows real promise, Martha. When he discovered that stories could be found in books, he set out to learn to read at once."

Soon the old house was quiet for the night as the master and his good wife crawled into feather beds for a much needed rest.

DING. DING. DING. DING. The hall clock was striking midnight when Richard awakened from a troubled

48

dream.

"Dicker! Dicker!" The urgent call rang sharply in his ears.

It was little Cäcilie! He must go to her at once.

"Yes—yes, I'm coming!" he cried, his teeth chattering with the cold as he searched frantically in the darkness for his clothes.

Now he must find the door that led out to the country road. Inch by inch he felt his way along the hall, the icy stones biting into his feet. Suddenly he stumbled against a heavy chair and crash—bang! it fell to the floor with loud clatter.

At the uproar the master leaped from his bed.

"Who's there?" he shouted. "I'll have you by the scruff of the neck, evil intruder!"

Holding a candle high over his nightcap, he peered into the darkness, his wife close behind with frightened eyes.

"Why—it's only the new little one!" she cried softly, hurrying toward him with open arms.

"No! No!" Richard drew back hastily, clutching his coat to him. "Cäcilie is calling me. I promised to come back for her."

His small face was white in the flickering candle glow, and his thin little body shook with the cold. As the hands drew nearer, he turned and sped down the hall with frightened cry, the schoolmaster close at his heels.

"Dicker, the new little puppies need someone, too," the soothing voice urged. "They will be howl-

50

ing with hunger as soon as daylight comes."

The piercing blue eyes turned in the shadows to search the kind face above. Slowly the fair head nodded.

"I—I think I can stay just long enough to feed them. Then I will take a puppy home to Cäcilie."

"We can decide in the morning, lad." The vicar gently led him to the high feather bed. "See, little one—this cozy nest is just big enough for a boy of six. Up you go!"

The heat made him drowsy and soon Richard was safely asleep. The morning brought cheering sunshine, and not only did he feed the puppies, but he chose the liveliest for his own.

The tiny ball of fluff followed him about with shrill barks, delighting his new master.

"I'll just wait until he is older before I take him to Cäcilie," he decided, at the urging of the director. "I think I'll call him Giant."

From then on, there was little trouble with the runaway. The moment the blue eyes grew anxious, the soft bundle crawling into his arms brought a sigh of contentment, and the young pupil turned to his lessons with a will.

He watched in wonder as winter winds heaped the snow into mountainous drifts. With happy cries the sleds were pulled out, and gay times there were sliding down the steep, frosty hillsides.

But best of all were the stories each night before bedtime. From the very beginning the favorite adventurer was Richard.

"It's Dicker's turn. Yes, Yes! Stories, Dicker!"

Waving his arms and shouting, or crouched with voice at a whisper, the young teller of tales held his audience in a trance. The stories grew ever more exciting, until gasps of fear or piercing cries brought a command from the master.

"Time for bed, gentlemen."

With scampering feet the listeners scattered like magic to hide under the covers, while chills of fright raced up and down young backs.

"A strange and rare power this boy has over others," declared Vicar Wetzel to his wife. "I have only to say 'If the lessons are done quickly, perhaps Richard will tell us a story.' And in record time the little scamps have finished their tasks."

The good Martha listened with a knowing smile, her grey curls bobbing.

"Ah yes, my dear. I, too, feel the mysterious strength of this child. In the blue eyes there shines a light that makes me stop and ponder." She paused to thread her needle. "But a delicate lad he is, with far too much sickness. And he needs more meat on his bones. Try as I will, I cannot fatten him up, so that his head always seems too large for his body, poor dear."

Now vacation time was at hand, and Richard's joy could scarcely be contained as he scrambled aboard the old red coach to ride home to Dresden.

"Dicker! Dicker! Dicker!" Glad cries welcomed him warmly as eager arms reached out to him. "How tall he has grown,— already like a little man!"

Richard dropped Giant into Cäcilie's lap and drew himself up proudly.

"I can read and write and spell and do sums and play two new pieces on the piano," he declared in one breath. "I know so much that I will never have to go to school again!"

He turned swiftly to the man he loved with all his heart.

"Now I can spend every single day in the theatre with you, father, and play real parts with the men."

Ludwig drew the slender figure into the circle of his arm and rested his head against the fair one.

"Ah, my dear lad, nothing would please me more than to have you always at my side," said he, gently. "But a man needs to know much to be a good actor, Richard. Work hard, boy, and in a few more years who knows what wonderful things might happen."

Mother Hannah listened thoughtfully.

"There will be plenty to keep you busy while you are here, Dicker," said she. "We move to a fine new home, where your father will have a splendid studio to paint his portraits."

With a shout Richard was off to explore the larger quarters owned by sword cutler Voigt, Cäcilie close at his heels. Right in front of the sweet shop it was, and with sighs of delight the two stood with noses flattened against the pane.

There was candy maker Orlandi in tall white hat, filling the window with mounds of rich chocolate puffs and green and white mint wheels, wondrous to behold.

His mouth watering at a sight so fair, Richard grasped the arm of his pigtailed companion.

"Oh, Cäcilie—if only we had some coins!" he sighed. A sudden idea made his eyes dance. "Don't move until you see me again," he commanded, running off at top speed.

In a short time he was back, holding out a handsome red leather book to the astonished sweet maker.

"It's for the chocolate puffs, sir," he explained eagerly. "You can see for yourself that it's far better than coins!"

The pale-faced storekeeper wiped his hands on his snowy apron and smiled broadly.

"Hm-m-m. Poems by Schiller. Well, well, well! Never have I had such payment for my wares," said he.

Chuckling merrily, he filled the small hands to overflowing with the creamy chocolate puffs and watched the delighted customers begin their happy feasting.

"But mind—no more books!" he cautioned, shaking a warning finger after them.

There was a whirl of excitement when the men came to carry beds and stoves and fat trunks and boxes to the new house. Richard raced upstairs and down, calling out orders at the top of his voice, to the amusement of the workmen.

But Mother Hannah sighed with relief when the moving was ended at last, and the pots and pans were stored away in the shining cupboards.

"Peace and quiet," said she, sinking wearily into a chair. "What a boon from the good Lord!"

The words had scarcely left her lips when piercing cries sent her flying to the doorway.

"WHOOP-LA! Look out below! Here comes the engine!"

Before her startled eyes, a small figure from the floor high above shot like a flash down the steeply winding banister. With a moan she covered her eyes to shut out the crashing fall.

But instead, merry laughter fell upon her ears.

"Come on, Cäcilie! We'll slide down even faster!"

Hannah ran to the staircase in alarm.

"Stop, Dicker, stop!" she cried, her eyes dark with fear. "You would soon be finished by so dangerous a pastime!"

But the temptation of the exciting rides was too great, and now and then Richard tried out his skill, always landing lightly and safely on his feet.

To his keen delight there were rapturous times in the theatre with his old friends, listening to rehearsals from the back seats and shouting "Louder!" with the director. As the late shadows fell over the city, he strode home with Ludwig, happier than a king.

All too quickly the exciting weeks were ended and he found himself back at the rambling school, telling of his gay adventures. Harder than ever he worked at his lessons, so that sooner he might take his place with his father in the theatre.

A long year went by, and one day as he bent over his sums, a messenger arrived at the door of the vicar.

"Ah, my dear boy, sad news has just come from your mother. Your father is not at all well, and you must return home at once," said the director gently. "I will go with you, Dicker. The coach leaves for Dresden in a few hours."

But Richard was already on his feet, crying out in distress as he pulled on his jacket.

"No, No! There is no time for waiting. I must go at once!"

"But the miles are too long, boy—far too long for

you to travel afoot."

Richard had not even heard the words. Running from the house, he found himself on the roadway, his heart pounding strangely within him. The dearest friend in all the world needed him. He must get to him swiftly.

The miles leading to the city were long indeed, and seemed never to end. But at last, just as the sun was setting in a sullen sky he arrived at his door, to be met by Mother Hannah.

"Dicker, your father is gravely ill," she whispered, her eyes wet with tears. "Come with me quickly." With noiseless step she led him to a small piano. "Play for him, child. He has asked to hear your little pieces."

All that night Richard tossed and turned in his bed, muttering in the dreams that would not let him rest. Just as the cold gray dawn stole through the lattice bars, the door opened softly and his mother came quietly to his side.

"Your father has gone far, far away from this earth, Dicker. He left you a message, my dear. He hoped that you would become a great man someday —perhaps a fine musician."

Richard stared into the sad face above him as the words made strange sounds in his ears. Surely they could not be true. Never again to hear the kind voice and feel the loving hand, and walk proudly at the side of his actor hero? Never to hear the cheery laugh and listen to the beautiful songs at eventide?

Suddenly he sat up, beating the air with his fists. A great cry sprang from his throat, a cry that rang sharply to every corner of the house.

"Father! Father! Father!"

The days were like a dream now, and Richard wandered about the city alone. Always his footsteps took him to the theatre, and he would remember and hurry away.

His home was filled with strange faces, and one man who looked a little like father Ludwig stopped him on the stairs one morning.

"You must be the young one called Richard," said he, smiling. "I am your stepfather's brother, and I have been wondering if you would like to go home with me for a visit. You would see more of your older brother, Julius, who is becoming quite a goldsmith in my workshop."

He took Richard's arm and led him to a chair.

"Who knows? Perhaps you might like the town well enough to settle down and live in Eisleben for the rest of your days."

Richard looked for a moment at the heavy man with sweeping moustache, busily twirling a thick golden chain around his finger.

"Oh, I couldn't, sir," he began earnestly. "You see, my mother can't get along without me now."

The big man slipped the shining links into his deep pocket and answered quietly.

"She has already said that you might come, lad." He lowered his voice to a whisper. "Did you know that there is a fine band right in the square, and a real circus now and then?"

Richard brightened at the thought.

"With acrobats doing tricks?" he questioned closely.

"Yes, indeed, and many more surprises. Do you think that you could leave with me at the end of the week?"

"Oh yes, sir!"

At last the morning arrived, and they were off in the frosty October dawn, leaving Dresden farther and farther behind as the sun climbed into the sky.

Late afternoon found the carriage at a small wayside inn, with a fierce dragon sign blowing in the wind.

"Change of horses," called the driver. "Everyone out."

Richard stood in the roadway, his eyes on the

lean, weary animals as the harness was quickly unfastened. How tired they were from their long, hard labor, and how patiently they waited for food and rest.

With a little cry he ran suddenly to the large brown creatures, patting them gently and resting his head against each in turn.

"Thank you," he murmured into the long, velvety ears. "Thank you for bringing me so far."

Uncle Geyer watched curiously, and smiled as his nephew carefully divided the packet of brown bread and butter that Mother Hannah had hastily prepared for the journey.

"There is a deal of good in this boy," said he to himself. "He has a kind and thoughtful heart."

In the eerie dead of night they arrived in the little town of Eisleben. But even then the market place was alive, country folk herding sleepy cows and sheep with throaty cries, and setting up stalls in the flickering torchlight.

Richard hung perilously from the carriage door, eager eyes feasting on the bustling scene before him.

"I don't suppose we could look around a little?" he ventured hopefully.

"Look around—at midnight!" Uncle Geyer groaned as he stretched his weary legs. "Plenty of time for exploring after a few hours of honest sleep, boy."

Richard picked up his bundles and soon found himself in a musty, dark passageway with a creaking door at the end.

How could he ever wait until morning for the adventures that were sure to be on every hand in this strange little town of Eisleben.

# CHAPTER THREE

In his small tower room overhanging the square, Richard awakened with a start. The bedclothes were dumped in a little heap on the floor, and he shivered and shook with the cold.

The fearful dream of wandering in endless dark caves was still in his mind as he peered across the tiny cubicle through the musty gloom.

Suddenly he remembered, and with a cry of relief bounded from his cot, wiping the sleep from his eyes.

"Eisleben! I'm in Eisleben, and it's time for exploring!"

Scurrying to his little battered trunk, he searched among his belongings for his old worn boots. It would never do to tramp on sharp cobbles in his

69

best Sunday pair, Mother Hannah had warned.

Rat-a-tat. Toot-toot. Rat-a-tat-tat-tat.

Gay sounds from the market below sent him flying to the door to listen.

It must be the band! Pounding drums and shrill blaring of trumpets echoed in the square as the old town clock struck the hour.

"I'm coming! I'm coming!"

With a glad cry Richard scrambled into his coat and scuttled down the steep back stairs. Across the dusty market place he flew and pushed his way through the crowd of townfolk.

His breath caught in his throat at the stirring spectacle before him. There, in splendid costume, the famous Hussar regiment was swinging into line,

coattails flying as the men piped a gay tune from the opera, *Der Freischütz*.

Richard darted from the curb and sprang to the side of a tall trumpeter.

"I know it! I already know the 'Huntsmen's Chorus'!" he shouted. "Herr Weber wrote the music, and he walks by my house in Dresden every day!"

But the player heard not a word as he tramped on briskly, lips glued to his shining instrument. Striding along with him, Richard sang with all his might around the square, feet scuffing proudly to the martial music.

"Company halt!"

At the crisp command he saluted smartly with

the men, and heart beating high, felt a part of the band as the trumpeter clapped him on the shoulder.

"A brave newcomer joining the ranks," he drawled to his comrades. "Welcome to the tooters' club, stranger."

Every morning from then on, Richard marched with the company, a tall hat perched on his fair head and a shining trumpet at his lips. His joy knew no bounds when at last he was allowed to lead the men, shouting strange commands to the proud Hussars.

"Eyes to the sun! Hats off to the clock! Bow to the steeple!" he barked.

At the grinning faces of the squad he burst into peals of laughter. Then, drawing himself up soberly, he led the players back to the barracks, ending the march with a flourish of the silver stick.

There was never a moment to be lonely. Even before daylight the market was filled with excitement, and soon there were friends on every hand.

Karl, the stout-armed baker, was always ready with a tasty breakfast.

"Rumblin' of me stummick tells me it's time for eatin'," he declared, drawing a paddle of fresh buns from the yawning mouth of the hot oven. "Have a bite with me, towhead. A man likes company."

The two sat together in peaceful silence in the early dawn, munching chunks of sweet bread and drinking from steaming bowls of liquid.

"Folks know you're about so early, pardner?"

"Oh no. Uncle Geyer and my big brother, Julius, are too busy pounding on gold to think much about boys. And the old cook sleeps most of the day."

As the sun drifted over the cobbles, the young explorer skipped off happily, sampling wares doled out to him: bright carrots and fresh cabbage leaves from the stall of buxom Frau Schwarz, or crisp raw potato and a handful of smoked sausage.

There were a few lessons with Uncle Geyer now and then. But most of the time he took little notice of his nephew, until one morning when he met him in the narrow passageway.

"Child!" he gasped, turning the grimy face to the light. "What would your home folk think of this terrible state of affairs? Quickly, young'un—your old grandmother must have a look at you."

In a few moments the carefree wanderer found himself before a low door.

"Enter quietly, lad, and wait until you are spoken to," said Uncle Geyer.

He was gone, and Richard slowly turned the knob and peered cautiously into the eerie, dark quarters.

"Who's there? Who's there, I say?" commanded a quavering voice from the far side of the room. "Come forward so that I can see you. But have a care—newcomers have just arrived."

Newcomers! They might be robbers, or even pirates! Stealing on tiptoe across the floor, Richard came upon Grandmother Geyer enthroned on a high chair, the back entwined with freshly cut boughs.

In and out of the low window darted a flock of birds that circled and fluttered about her with gay songs and twitterings.

"Softly, boy, softly!" She turned keen gray eyes on him. "So—you must be Ludwig's stepson. I have been hearing about you, child."

She held out her hand in welcome, but at sight of the grubby fingers, drew back with a grimace.

"Lackaday! An urchin to greet his grandmother! Come with me at once. But mind sharply—do not disturb my family here."

In a tiny back room she drew him to a wooden bucket of rain water, and scrubbed and scoured and rinsed him until he cried out in alarm.

"Now for a bit of reward, child. You may watch the family that God has sent me. But gently! Tread very gently."

Richard could not believe his eyes as he sat crouched on the floor near his grandmother. The moment she reached her chair the birds gathered about her, settling themselves on her arms and shoulders, clamoring to be fed.

"Not a mouthful shall you have, my beauties, until you have performed in style for the gentleman here. Come now, dearies," she coaxed. "One for a fly, two for fleas, and three for fat bugs that live in the trees."

Little tricks she had taught them, and a rarer sight Richard had never seen as they darted about her finger in whirring circles, filling the air with trilling song at her bidding. A few, with pale yellow vests, hopped up the steps of a tiny ladder to a red tree house above.

Every day from then on, Richard crept eagerly into his grandmother's room. His heart was filled to overflowing when at last he, too, was allowed to train the feathered visitors and cut fresh boughs for the special chair and china stove.

But sad was the time when he found his snow-haired friend in tears at the loss of one of her pets.

"The cat—that wicked old Tom with the evil green eye it was. Like a thief he snatched the tender nestling with the scarlet waistcoat. He is no more, no more," she wept.

Her new helper tried his best to comfort her.

"Never mind, Grandmother. I'll find you a prettier one, even lovelier than Redcoat," he promised.

By the hour he sat outside in the small courtyard, coaxing feathered creatures to his hand. At last he captured a baby woodpecker and carried it in triumph to the enraptured old lady.

"Ah, you are a good boy with a kind heart, and I shall adopt you, Richard. From this day on, I name you 'Second Grand Trainer of Bird Kingdom.'"

But the happy days came suddenly to an end one morning when the bird trainer found himself marched off to the country school by Uncle Geyer. The boys in heavy boots eyed him sullenly and called him Square Head.

Many a battle there was, the new pupil learning to use his fists for the first time.

Poor Richard. Twisting and turning on the hard bench, he heard very little of the lessons droning endlessly in his ears. At last, with scampering feet at the closing bell, he raced headlong from the stuffy room to wander along the rocky banks of the river Unstrut.

"I am free, free, free!" he sang to the wind. Pulling off his shoes, he let his feet sink deep into the velvety emerald moss with a blissful sigh.

Late one afternoon he came upon a tipsy old raft of three logs and claimed it for his own. What fun it was to pole himself along, and discover new inlets with fresh water racing below, threatening to wash him overboard.

"Ship ahoy—coming into port!" he called, steering into a shallow cove for a rest.

With the trees forming a little house around him, he was well content in his snug hideaway. There he lay, watching the families of minnows dart about in the deep green pocket of water below.

Hours he whiled away, spinning wonderful tales in his mind until the cooling gray mist crept like a ghost across the water, telling him it was time to leave for the night.

For two happy weeks there was no school, and Richard awakened one morning to find the market square buzzing with excitement. There, before his very eyes, a whole troupe of acrobats was performing in gay-colored tights.

Head over heels they whirled, tumbling over each other, flying through blazing hoops of fire and, best of all, walking on a rope stretched from tower to tower.

Richard gasped at the daring stunts, and held his breath as a man in purple not only walked on the high, thin line, but danced and rode on wheels as easily as though he were on solid ground.

"Bravo! Bravo! Bravo!" cheered the crowd lustily as the performer bowed low and calmly climbed

down the tall ladder.

Nothing in the whole world could be greater than walking on a tight-rope, decided Richard.

The very next day as soon as it was light, he set to work. Quickly gathering together a pile of twine, he patiently wove the strands over and over until at last the bumpy line was long enough to span the small courtyard. Tying it tightly to the corner posts, he was ready to try out his handmade rope.

If only he had a purple costume, how fine it would be. Ah well, his underwear would have to do.

Pulling off his coat and trousers, he climbed the clumsy ladder and gingerly tested the line with his bare feet. Now he had only to balance himself with the pole that he had whittled from a young sapling.

Better not look down, he told himself. Acrobats kept their eyes straight ahead and just tripped along airily. Taking a deep breath, he counted slowly:

"One-two-three-" and bravely stepped out into space.

Poor Richard. The next thing he knew, he was flying through the air and landing with a terrible thud in the courtyard below. Too frightened to cry out, he lay gasping for breath.

"Acrobats never whimper!" he told himself sternly.

When he was able to move about, he was on his feet, painfully climbing the ladder for a fresh start. Again and again he plummeted to the hard cobbles and, bruised and sore, crept into bed without a word, only to try once more the next day.

Early one morning Grandmother Geyer stepped out into the courtyard in search of a pet sparrow.

Glancing up suddenly, she shrieked in horror and clapped her hands to her head. A scrawny little figure was walking in the sky, with only a slender reed to balance himself!

"Oh, Oh! Heaven help us all! A dead child to take home to his mother!" she wailed.

Suddenly a shrill cry startled her from her misery.

"Look, Grandmother—I did it! I can walk the tight-rope! Now I'll never have to do it again!"

Long, happy months of the strange and wonderful life in little Eisleben came to an end one wintry day when Uncle Geyer called from his workshop, "A letter from your mother, boy."

Putting on his square spectacles, he unfolded the sheets carefully. "She sends an invitation from your own father's people, inviting you to visit them on your way home to Dresden."

Richard kicked a stone at his feet and his face clouded.

"But I'd rather stay here now, Uncle Geyer," he declared, edging to the doorway of the small workroom.

"Ah yes, lad, and lonely enough it will be without you. But we had better follow your mother's directions. In the morning the coach will be along to carry you to Leipzig."

Richard grasped his uncle's arm, his face suddenly aglow.

"Leipzig!" he cried. "Why, that's the very place where I was born!"

He was off with a shout to spread the startling news through the market place. Then, back in his small room, he carefully packed his treasures by candle light, to be ready when the time came to leave.

It seemed as if everyone in the whole countryside had come to say farewell. And so early in the morning, too, with giant snowflakes whirling through the dark, frosty air.

He waved from the window of the coach and called, "I'm off on a great adventure to the place where I was born! But I'll be back to see you all some day soon."

One by one the smiling faces were lost from sight, and out on the country road sudden sharp loneliness swept over the young passenger.

Little Eisleben was slipping away behind him, and he longed to jump from the coach and run back to the dear place that had been his home for more than a year.

The warm bundle in his hands made him look down suddenly. His present from the baker!

Tearing off the covering, his eyes lighted happily on the pile of freshly baked raisin buns. Carefully he divided them with the children and was soon chewing contentedly on the sweet bread until not a crumb was left in sight.

The lurching of the coach made him drowsy as the dawn began to lighten the dingy windows. Slowly his head slid to rest against a basket of young hens from the market, and all the cares of the world flew away as he fell fast asleep.

The sturdy horses jogged on and on and at last, with a fresh burst of speed, they pulled their burden into the big city of Leipzig.

Dicker sat up with a start as the door swung open and his name rang sharply in his ears.

"Richard! Richard Wagner!"

There, just outside stood Uncle Adolph with his

sister, Aunt Friederike Wagner with hands outstretched.

"Welcome! Welcome, dear nephew!" His aunt, smelling of delicate cologne, took his arm. "Ah, here is the carriage. Perhaps you would like to drive past the inn where you were born, Richard."

"Oh, yes!" agreed the eager young traveler. "And the place where my father was head of all the policemen, too."

"Not head of the police, boy," corrected his uncle. "He was an official of the city of Leipzig. But he wanted the policemen to do their work well, so he kept their records in good order."

Richard listened carefully, drinking in the words about his own father.

"And above all, he loved the theatre and spent much of his spare time watching plays. It was his good actor friend, Ludwig Geyer, who was to become your kind stepfather," said Uncle Adolph.

They rolled along the wide avenue in the comfortable carriage, and with all his heart Richard longed to climb up with the coachman and view the sights of the city from on high.

But the brakes closed down suddenly, bringing

them to a halt before a simple inn with the sign over the door: RED AND WHITE LION.

"There, child, in that very room on the second floor you were born on a stormy May morning," explained Uncle Adolph. "And a frail little baby when your father carried you to the St. Thomas church, to be christened Wilhelm Richard Wagner. Never was anyone more proud of his new man-child."

The young listener sat peering intently at the windows above, and as the horses stepped along briskly, he sighed contentedly. It was high honor, indeed, to have had a father who looked after the police in the big city of Leipzig.

"Home at last!" announced Aunt Friederike as the carriage stopped before the big Thome House.

Home! Richard looked about him in awe. It was like the town hall or a castle, with room after room opening before him. And the hearty meal of meat dumplings was served on the biggest table that he had ever seen.

But weary with traveling, his eyes began to feel heavy before the fruit pudding was half finished.

"Come, child, it is time the long day was ended," said his aunt, leading him up a broad staircase. Far off in one corner of the mansion the candle halted.

"This apartment has been made ready for your visit, dear nephew. It is the one that the king occupies when he is in Leipzig. I hope that you will be comfortable here."

Richard eyed the monstrous bed, hung in richest silks and velvets, with down cushions piled high.

"But twenty people could sleep in it, easily!" he exclaimed.

All around the room was heavy furniture, and portraits of hoop-skirted ladies and men with swords. They seemed to fasten their eyes on him, and looking away hastily, Richard flung off his clothes and climbed the steps to the great bed.

Down, down, down he sank in the feathery lightness, until only the tip of his nose could be seen.

"I will draw the curtains around you, my dear, so that you will be cozy and snug." The words were faint in his ears. "Good night, lad, and God keep you safe."

Out went the flickering candle, and the darkness swallowed him in one big gulp. The cushions were smothering him so that he could not breathe, and he struck out with his arms to rid himself of the

hot puffiness.

Suddenly Richard gasped in alarm. Something was stalking through the curtains! The people in the portraits were coming to life and dozens of eyes were glaring down at him. Now their mouths were beginning to leer in a horrible way, and shaking with fright, he threw the thick coverlet over his head.

"Let me alone! Oh, go away and let me be!" he moaned.

But the arms were already reaching under the bedclothes, and he screamed in terror and broke into wildest sobbing.

Somehow he must free himself from the dreadful creatures. With a mighty struggle he crawled to the railing and fell headlong to the floor.

Quickly! Under the monstrous bed while there was still time. They could never find him there. Raising himself, he rolled over and over, and in the

musty darkness fell into deep, troubled dreams.

The faint rays of morning light awakened him, and trembling with cold, he crawled back into the big bed. It would never do to let his aunt know of the terrors of the night.

Never was Richard so happy as when the short visit came to an end and he found himself on the way home to Dresden.

Christmas time! A whistle of joy piped from his lips at the very thought, and the coach passengers smiled at their excited young companion.

"Four more days! Four, four, four." He broke into a song of his own making. "Only four more days and Christmas will be here!"

# CHAPTER FOUR

"I'm home again! Home, home, home!" With a shout of joy Richard bounded into the warm, comfortable rooms that he loved so well.

All was astir with holiday preparations, and Mother Hannah beamed on the new arrival as she mixed Christmas cookies in the brown wooden bowl.

"Ah, Dicker, the best gift of all is to have you here with us," she declared happily. "See, child, you and Cäcilie may cut the dough in stars and attend to the baking, while I start the fruit pudding."

She paused and wiped her hands.

"But do not forget that in the morning you must be on your way to the grammar school, my son."

Richard's cry of distress tore at her heart.

"Oh no, Mother! After Christmas I will begin.

93

Just three days until the holiday is finished, and then you will see how hard I will work!"

But Hannah shook her head firmly. She must not spoil this child.

"The master has already sent word for you to come, Dicker. But you may get up very early if you wish, to help with the trimming before you leave."

With excited whispers the two youngest members stole from their beds before dawn the next morning, to sort the Christmas ornaments and start to decorate the spicy green fir.

"Chil - dren! Time for morning prayers."

Sadly Richard took himself into the large bed-room to join the older members of the family, cir-cled around Mother Hannah. In her nine woolen caps she sat up very straight in the high bed, looking over her brood to see that all was well.

"Richard will recite the prayer this morning," she directed briskly. "Then we will sing our favorite hymn before I take my morning coffee."

The verse was quickly finished and lovely voices filled the room in a fine old hymn, and the short service was over.

"Now, Richard, it is time for you to leave," said Mother Hannah, pouring a steaming cup of liquid. "Albert will go with you to the Kreuz School. Be sure to mind your manners, my son."

There was no escape. Bundled in heavy coat, with blue scarf blowing in the icy wind, he ran at his older brother's side and soon found himself in the dreaded building.

The brusque headmaster in stiff collar eyed the new pupil closely and handed him a small red book.

"I would like to hear you read, young man, and then do a few sums, so that we will know where to place you in this famous old Kreuz School of Dresden."

Poor Richard. He tried his best, but very little of the page could he read correctly. The sums were no better, and the master shook his head in despair at the spelling.

Taking Albert aside, he spoke in low tones.

"A very sad state of affairs, indeed. This boy has learned very little in his nine years. We will allow him to enjoy the festival season before telling him the truth of the matter."

And enjoy the holidays Richard did to the full. Shivering with delight, he and Cäcilie found a dizzy swirling rain of snowflakes to greet them on Christmas morning.

A merry day it was, with laughter and feasting and opening of gifts. Richard watched with bated breath as his offerings were unwrapped: two pressed butterfly wings for his mother, and smooth, pale-colored stones from the river bed in Eisleben for

96

his brother and sisters.

"Now it's your turn, Cäcilie," he directed. "I hope you like my present, because it's the best of all."

The littlest member gingerly raised the lid of the brown box, and screamed in terror as a giant bull-frog leaped halfway across the room.

"Back, Alexander!" At the command the fat creature turned and with a low "Gallerump," hopped directly to his former master.

"He's trained!" cried Richard proudly. "It took days and nights to do it, too, on my bed at Uncle Geyer's. Isn't he a beauty, Cäcilie? Now you can have people come and watch him do tricks."

All too soon the beautiful holiday was at an end, and in his fine new Christmas jacket, Richard took himself back to the Kreuz School to begin his lessons.

The hours passed quickly by, and as darkness began to fall, Mother Hannah looked anxiously down the snowy roadway.

"It is long past time for the child to be at home," she declared. "You had better go after your brother, Albert. Something must have gone wrong."

Just as he was about to leave, Cäcilie raced into the kitchen.

"He's here, Mother, in the back storeroom!" she cried. "And he won't even look at me!"

Everyone hurried down the narrow stairs and gathered around the figure crouched in the far corner.

"Dicker! Dicker!" Mother Hannah leaned over him in alarm. "What is it, child? Has something hurt you?"

The only answer was the sound of weeping. Suddenly Richard turned fiercely, his eyes flashing through a rain of tears.

"I'm a dunce, Mother—a terrible dunce! Even the master said so. He says I know nothing at all!" His voice choked with angry sobs. "He put me in the lowest class, and everyone laughed and called me 'Baby Dunce'!"

It was long before he could be coaxed back to the school, and no amount of urging could make him do sums or learn to spell.

And now his nights were even worse than his days at school. As in Leipzig, the furniture seemed to come alive and pounce upon him until he screamed in terror, waking everyone around him.

Hannah, in long grey dressing gown, hurried to the small room with soothing tones.

"See, Dicker, the lighted candle will chase the shadows away, so that you will have nothing to fear," she comforted, tucking the covers around the trembling shoulders.

Mother Hannah was glad when the springtime came and she could make her little trips into the countryside. Tying on her bonnet one morning, she called:

"Dicker and Cäcilie, if you do not keep me waiting, you may go with me to Loschwitz today."

With a shout of joy Richard scrambled into his jacket, and the three were off. In gay spirits they rode into the pale golden sunlight, out to the fresh countryside, with sweep of green fields and trees washed clean with the night's light rainfall.

In no time at all they were in the little village, lying sleepily beside the river Elbe in a glow of yellow light.

"Do not wander too far away," cautioned Mother Hannah. "And be sure that you are back at the cottage by sundown."

She was off on her errands, her basket swinging on her arm, and with scampering feet Richard led Cäcilie down to the boats along the water front. Old boats and new, little craft and big were examined with keenest delight, and to crown their joy a lazy ride on a low flat barge ended the morning.

With a shout and heels flying, Richard was off to

the sweet-smelling meadows.

"We'll hunt for birds' nests and snakes and fat worms for fishing," he cried, turning a round of somersaults.

Through the hours the two explored the peaceful countryside to their hearts' content, shoes hung over shoulders. Never were spring flowers more beautiful, and the trilling song of meadow larks made their hearts beat fast with delight.

As the shadows began to fall, they found themselves near an old barn. Suddenly Richard stopped short, finger in air.

"Listen, Cile—do you hear the crying? Something is hurt!"

They crept to the side of the building, and there in a low trough was a new-born puppy, splashing and barking piteously.

"Oh, Dicker, save him! Save him!" Cäcilie's wails of anguish drowned out the little cries.

Richard's hands were already in the water, lifting out the tiny creature and placing it gently on the ground.

"Another minute and it would have been gone forever," he declared. "We'll just wrap it up and take it along with us."

Soon the puppy was snug and warm in his woolen cap, and the two explorers set out for the pathway that would take them back to little Loschwitz for the night. Already the glorious sunset colors were fading from the sky and they hastened their footsteps, Richard shifting the small bundle and telling tales to while away the time.

"No need to be afraid, Cile," said he as darkness gathered softly around them. "No fear at all—except passing that old graveyard!"

At the very words, his gentle companion clung

to him desperately and set up such a loud wailing that he, himself, felt stabs of fright at the thought of the most terrible ghosts of all, lying in wait for them.

Suddenly the sound of wheels made them stop short and there, looming from the darkness at the side of the road, was an old man in a ramshackle cart.

"Oh, sir!" cried Richard, "could you carry us, please? We weigh so little the horses wouldn't even know we were there!"

The farmer bent down to look into the eager, smudged face.

"Well, now, guess we could take on a mite of weight," he mused, chewing a long spear of marsh grass. "Up with you, then, strangers. No time for wastin'."

To his astonishment, as they jogged past the cemetery wall his young passengers began to shout at the top of their voices, shaking their fists in air.

"Horrid old ghosts! Silly old ghosts! Can't catch us now! Ha, Ha, Ha!"

Thanks to the old man, they were safely at the cottage and all was well. Hastily the puppy was hidden in the big bed and tenderly covered with the best blanket for the night.

Early the next morning, hearing strange sounds, Mother Hannah came upon the tiny creature, crying hungrily to be fed.

"Upon my word! A strange dog, and in the very best bed! Oh, what will the landlady think of this terrible state of affairs?"

Cautiously two heads appeared from behind an old chest.

"Oh, mother, isn't he a beauty?" cried Richard,

beaming. "We were just going to feed him before we take him home to Dresden."

"Dresden! The house is quite full enough without an extra animal to care for. The landlady will see that he has a good home."

A full and busy household it was, indeed, with Albert and Rosalie and Clara all actors and singers. Every day they talked of the theatre, and little else did Richard hear.

"With all my heart I hope this son will not make the stage his life work," she declared. "If only we could find out what he would like to be."

Very soon it seemed that she would know.

One afternoon when Richard had settled himself in school for a dreaded lesson in grammar, the director appeared suddenly.

"Young men, I bring you a sad task to perform," he began, balancing his spectacles on his nose. "Each student will write a poem about your dear comrade, Starke, who has just gone to heaven. The best work will be printed for everyone to read."

Richard sat up with a start. A poem, and set up in print!

Eagerly he reached for his pen and lines began to form down the paper. On and on he wrote until long shadows had crept over the table. Startled, he discovered that he was alone in the darkening room, and hastily carried his offering to the master's desk.

From then on, earlier than usual each morning, Richard took his place in the old building. His eyes were on the door, his ears listening for the news that he longed to hear.

At last one morning the headmaster arrived, and

after calling the names in a singsong voice he paused, looking thoughtfully over his spectacles.

"Young gentlemen, we have selected the poem that will be read by all of the people of Dresden—a great honor for the Kreuz School."

There was hushed silence, every eye on the director.

"You will be glad to hear that the scholar who brings us this honor is Richard."

"Bravo! Bravo! Richard!" Calls and cheers rang around him as the young author sat with a smile on his lips.

But best of all were the quiet words of his mother.

"God be thanked. The boy will be a poet some day," she declared fervently, her warm brown eyes filling with happy tears.

Richard was delighted with his new honor and turned to his lessons with a will. Very little free time did he have, and he jumped for joy when the master announced one morning:

"All work and no play makes poor scholars, so the rest of the day you may spend as you wish. Enjoy it, gentlemen."

With dizzy shouts the boys raced out into the

sunlight, throwing their caps high in air. Richard danced and leaped with the crowd and in a frenzy of delight, caught a cap as it flew over his head.

"Up you go!" he shrieked, and with a mighty fling sent it sailing onto the schoolhouse roof.

"Oh, my cap! My cap!" wailed Hans, tears falling over his plump cheeks. "And a heavy stick on me for losing it!"

Terror struck at Richard's heart and he was off in a flash. At all costs the cap must be brought back before it was too late.

Up the stairs to the high loft he scrambled and gingerly stepped out onto the dangerous roof ledge. At sight of him, the boys set up a mighty shout.

"There he is! Oh, he will surely fall! Run for the porter and his ladder to rescue him. Hurry!"

But Richard was not to be stopped. The cap was high above him and kicking off his shoes, he started up the steep roof on all fours. Suddenly he began to slip and slide, and catching his breath in alarm, flattened himself quickly.

In a moment he was on his way again, moving grimly inch by inch. Cautiously he reached out with his hand and feeling the cap at last, placed it be-

tween his teeth. Then, at snail's pace he edged his way back to the small opening and eased himself gently to the dark safety inside.

The old porter was grumbling angrily as he climbed up the narrow ladder after his charge. And startled almost out of his wits when a wiry figure jumped out at him from the shadows, asking sweetly:

"Pray tell, are you looking for someone—or a bird, perhaps?"

The grim servant looked down at the impishly grinning Richard and struck out with his hand.

"Pray tell, indeed!" he growled. "I'm looking for a bird, right enough—a gallows bird!"

At home, Mother Hannah waited hopefully for more poems to come from the pen of her son. But instead, Richard began to read stories of Greek heroes, shivering with delight at the thrilling adventures.

But still he was not satisfied. To know how the heroes really spoke to one another, he must learn their own language. At once he took himself to the master, who looked at his earnest pupil with puzzled frown.

"Greek!" he exclaimed. "A most difficult study, young man. But if you must learn it, we will find someone to teach you."

Richard was delighted and set to work with a will. After long months of patient struggle he was happy beyond words when he could speak and read in the Greek tongue.

One evening as he sat in his small room, an idea swept into his mind. Why not write some of the stories back into his own language? From the Greek tongue into the German tongue!

With a zest he started on the tremendous task, working night after night until the candle sputtered and went out.

Mother Hannah looked closely at the pale, weary face each morning.

"Dicker, we must see that you have more rest, and plenty of good food to fatten you up a bit," said she.

Thick slices of black bread and hot porridge came in a steady stream until he cried out in alarm.

"Stop, Mother, stop! Already I am beginning to waddle like a stuffed goose!"

Carefully shielding the light, he went on with his

work. Scratch, scratch, scratch, flew his pen over the paper in the flickering candle glow.

At last, in great pride one morning he took the thick tablets to Master Sillig, who could scarcely believe his eyes.

"I would not have dreamed it possible!" The kind teacher arose and put his hands on the shoulders of his thirteen-year-old student. "This is truly a man-sized task, and very proud I am of such a scholar. Another great honor you bring to the Kreuz School."

The praise rang in his ears for days and Richard was well content. But Mother Hannah was still worried.

"A good thing that the summer is at hand." She nodded her wise head slowly. "The boy needs a long rest. I'll just stir up his favorite fruit pudding as a little surprise."

But one day of idleness was enough for Richard. With Cäcilie he set out to play tricks on everyone in the household. Shoe toes were stuffed with pebbles and beds laden with grasshoppers; toads leaped out of cupboards, and strange insects, taken out of pockets, crawled over the tablecloth in the middle of the dinner.

At the shrieks of dismay the two culprits shouted with laughter.

"This will never do!" Mother Hannah shook a warning finger at the mischief-makers. "One more trick, and not a mouthful of apple pudding will you have."

A few days later, stretched lazily in the small gar-

den behind the house, Richard turned to his companion.

"Do you suppose there is a heaven where animals go when they die?" He paused and stroked the pet beside him. "If there is, Bones and his dog brothers should have a chance to get there."

His eyes began to sparkle, and with a cautious look around he murmured, "Cile—there's work to be done!"

Noiselessly he led the way into the kitchen and peering into the cooling chest, spied a large piece of tender, juicy meat, carefully prepared for the evening meal.

"This will do the trick," he whispered, carefully putting it into a wire basket and binding it securely to the collar of Bones.

"Now we'll give all the poor dogs a chance to get to heaven," explained the plotter, a plan growing in his mind. "They will follow the meat for sure, and we'll lead them all to paradise."

Up and down the streets they roamed, and before an hour had passed, fat and lean dogs, grey dogs and spotted dogs were in a long procession behind the meat carrier.

"There should be enough now," decided Richard. Turning down a narrow alley, he led the way back home.

The scrambling, yelping heap in the small back yard brought Mother Hannah running to the window. Throwing up her hands, she cried out in dismay, "Richard! Richard! What are all those animals doing here?"

The dog trainer waved his arms and grinned happily.

"Oh, Mother, wait until you see! We're teaching them to do tricks in my play called 'Dog Heaven.' The owners will come to see them perform. Then we can buy each one a shining silver collar, and when they go home again they will have a much better life."

"Richard!" Mother Hannah cut in sharply with a stern command. "Take every single animal home this very minute! Their poor masters will be frantic when they find them gone."

Something must be done to stop this young madcap, she decided. When the last stray dog had been returned, she looked sternly at her youngest son.

"You have behaved very badly, indeed," she declared solemnly. "As punishment there will be no theatre for you this evening, young man."

A loud wail greeted her words. Not to hear his favorite opera *Der Freischütz,* with singing and acting and splendid scenery on the great stage? Even now the tunes were beginning to sing in his mind. Ah, how lovely they were!

Perhaps he could learn to play some of the melodies by ear. He was at the piano in a trice, stumbling over parts of the music and making up an accompaniment with his left hand.

Suddenly hurrying footsteps sounded behind him.

"Hush! Hush, Richard! The master, himself, is here!"

The young pianist turned swiftly and caught his

mother's arm.

"Herr Weber, the composer of *Der Freischütz?*"

"Yes, yes! He comes for a little visit with your sister Clara, to speak of her splendid singing in the opera house."

Richard crept into the room to gaze in awe at the composer, whose work was sweeping through the city of Dresden.

"So—this must be the player of my melodies." A warm smile lighted Herr Weber's delicate face as he looked down into the piercing blue eyes. "You wish to become a musician, lad?"

Mother Hannah answered quickly for him.

"My son has never shown any talent for music, sir."

With bated breath Richard stole to the window to watch the noted visitor limp painfully down the steps.

"Cäcilie," he whispered, "there goes the greatest man on earth! Someday I will write an opera, too, for the whole world to hear, just like Herr Weber."

With a joyous cry he sped to the kitchen.

"Mother! I could have the master's music for my very own with just a few groschen!" he exclaimed, his eyes wide with longing. "The coins would buy music paper, and I could copy the compositions and keep them forever!"

Mother Hannah studied the matter carefully.

"Funds are hard to come by, my son. But if you are truly in earnest, and do not waste a single sheet, perhaps—"

With a shout, Richard's arms were around her in a warm hug, and off he ran for the coveted, precious paper.

Long days he spent copying the borrowed work of the master and was proud, indeed, when the last note was neatly and carefully set down. Hurrying to the piano, he struggled harder than ever to play the composer's music.

Mother Hannah, busy in one corner of the house, stopped to listen. Had the time come to really work with a teacher, she wondered. The boy must have every chance to learn.

Before many days had passed, Richard himself was welcoming the new master.

"Oh, Herr Humann, I want to play the opening of Herr Weber's opera," he cried, eagerly turning the pages of the newly copied overture. "Tell me,

119

please, where do I find the notes?"

As before, Richard would have none of the exercises to help the fingers move smoothly. After a few months the weary master went in search of Mother Hannah, who was busily preparing the evening meal.

"Ah, madam, the young colt must follow his own headstrong way," he sighed, patting his few locks into place. "A great pianist he will never be. But strange that he seems to know what to do, with little help from me."

It was true. In a short time his pupil was playing the most difficult music.

"A splendid thing to be able to read whatever you wish," agreed his teacher, watching the fingers fly over the keys. "But what a pity all is so poorly done. Ah, my ears! How they ache, long after I have left you."

Richard looked up swiftly, hands in mid-air.

"But sir, there is no time to go over and over the pieces, with so much music in the whole world to play!"

There were no more lessons with the master, but the pounding at the instrument never ceased.

Even at night, the eager young pianist sat with the difficult opera books of his sisters before him. With a flourish he played the accompaniments and airily sang the solo parts as well, beating out the time with one foot.

The members of the family laughed heartily and gathered around the piano to watch and listen.

"Such an artist, and so much noise! He stumbles well, yes?" they cried.

But Mother Hannah came swiftly to the rescue.

"Richard has learned much in a very short time," she reminded the amused audience. "Some day you may be very proud of your young brother."

Dicker was well satisfied. He had finished what he had set out to do. Now the whole world of music was open to him and he could explore the works of the great masters to his heart's content.

And glory there was on Sunday afternoons when

he could steal away to the Grosser Garten to hear Zillman's band. With Cäcilie at his side, he crept closer and closer to the players to watch them tune their instruments.

Chills ran up and down his spine as the martial music began, and not once did he move until the last note of his favorite pieces echoed through the shadowy gardens. With a deep sigh of contentment, he stole home through the quiet streets with his gentle companion.

Very seldom were the two far away from each other.

"Dicker! Dicker!" rang the call through the house one rainy afternoon as Cäcilie went in search of her brother.

Suddenly she came upon him in a little hideaway under the stairs, his eyes glued to the pages of a book.

"It's by Shakespeare, the greatest writer of plays," he whispered. "There are ghosts, Cile—deadly fiends that stalk about in the dark of night."

Down the narrow stairway he led her to his favorite dim corner, where they would not be disturbed.

"Cäcilie! I'm going to write the greatest play in all the world—even greater than Shakspeare!" Richard leaned closer to his faithful comrade. "Only you will hear it, and a terrible tale it will be, with many who must die!"

The blue eyes closed to slits and his mouth tightened as the author wrote furiously. From then on, every moment of his spare time was spent at his task, and now and then he read bits of the new work in a whisper to his frightened companion.

"How many are dead now, Dicker?" she asked in awe as the scribbling stopped for a moment.

"Forty-two," was the grim reply. "And now I'll have to bring back a few as ghosts, because there are no more characters for the last act."

But the work was not to be finished, not for a long time to come.

One evening Mother Hannah settled her family around a steaming chicken pie, and after serving each one plentifully, she put down the heavy ladle.

"My dears, Rosalie has just been called to sing in the theatre in Prague," she announced quietly. "A week from tomorrow we will go there to live. Much there will be to get ready, and even the youngest

members must have willing hands.''

Richard started to his feet with a delighted cry.

"A new home in a new city!" he exclaimed. "And no more lessons at the Kreuz School!''

Mother Hannah quickly laid her hand on his arm.

"Ah, my son, you will remain here in Dresden for a time, so that your work at the splendid school will not have to stop," she explained. "But you will enjoy living with the Böhme family. They have promised to look after you very well.''

Richard was puzzled for a moment. Then his face lightened in a bright smile. At last he would be a man of the world, able to manage some of his own affairs.

And plenty of excitement there was sure to be at the lively home of his mischievous, fun-loving comrades.

# CHAPTER FIVE

"Up with you, sleepyhead! Time for boating in the moonlight!"

"Boating! But it's the middle of the night!"

Richard opened one eye to find his friend Rudolf bending over him with impish grin, a candle in one hand.

"Night-time, day-time—what matter as long as there is revelry!"

With a sweep the covers were rudely torn from the bed, and bright laughter rang in his ears as Richard scrambled from his warm nest to join the party of young folk.

Life at the Böhme home was different from anything that he had ever known, with lusty dancing, singing, playing of jokes, and going on excursions at any hour.

Very little rest there was and through the months

the lessons were poor, indeed, and Master Sillig spoke sternly to his young student.

"Richard, there will be no place for you at the Kreuz School if you do not speedily mend your ways, young man."

But the bright sunny days only brought gay picnics and exploring the deep forests, and a great longing to journey to faraway places.

"Rudolf!" exclaimed Richard one morning, "why do we not pay mother a little visit in Prague? She would be overjoyed to see us."

"An excellent plan!" agreed his friend. "A bit of a walk, my lad, but plenty of adventure in the Bohemian Mountains."

The very next morning the two were on their way, with few coins in their pockets. But a goodly supply of bread and cheese hung over their shoulders against hours of hunger.

Singing and laughing heartily, they strode away, never dreaming of the hardships ahead.

Night-time found them footsore and weary, and crawling into a pile of hay in an old barn, they were soon fast asleep. But daylight awakened them all too soon, taking them on their way again.

Now the hours seemed longer than ever, and the hot sun rays burned into their very bones.

"I am as hungry as a scraggly crow," moaned Richard. "And not enough coins to buy the simplest meal."

"And Prague still a long way off," added Rudolf with a sigh.

No sooner had they flung themselves by the dusty roadside to rest, than the sound of voices and grinding wheels from a byway broke the hot silence. Pulling himself to his knees, Richard peered around a little thicket.

"Two beautiful ladies," he reported softly. "And riding in a handsome carriage with silken cushions!"

Rudolf sat up quickly, grasping the arm of his companion.

"Dicker! Why not ask the travelers for a few groschen to help us on our way?"

"Begging, Rudolf!"

"Beg or starve, my fine fellow. Besides, you would ask so sweetly, they would be flattered. I'll just take myself off."

As quick as a rabbit he was hidden in the bushes, and Richard found himself in the middle of the roadway, red cotton cap on his head and blue linen blouse hanging limply from his shoulders.

"If you please, a few coins would keep two poor wanderers from cruel death this day," he pleaded, his cheeks burning and eyes on the ground.

The women spoke together in low tones.

"He does not look like a beggar, sister. Ah, no. But he seems done for, poor lad." The older woman filled the outstretched hand with groschen. "There, boy, 'twill help a little. God speed you on your way."

New life surging through him, Richard sped back to his companion as the carriage rolled on.

"We are rich, Rudy! Will it be dinner at the lodge yonder, or a good bed for the night?"

It did not take long to decide, and the travelers soon found themselves at a table near the turning spits, enjoying such a feast as they had not had in many a day.

Just as they were finishing a tasty pudding, in sauntered a strolling player with jingling bell atop his pointed hood and gaily painted harp strapped to his back.

He strode to Richard's side and tapped him on the shoulder.

"Innkeeper says you start for Prague at dawn. I

join you for company," he announced briskly. "They call me first minstrel of the mountain, but you shall judge for yourself when I have had my fill."

Speedily he devoured great chunks of meat, washed down with plenty of wine, and tuning the strings of his harp, settled himself for long playing.

With a strumming sweep he began, head thrown back, eyes closed to slits as the wild Gypsy music filled the smoky, torchlit room.

Richard sat spellbound on the floor, listening to

such melodies as he had never heard before—now
haunting and sad, the next moment so stirring that
he could scarcely keep from frenzied shouting.

On into the night the minstrel sang and played
like a madman, holding his audience in a trance.
Faster and ever more wild grew his music until, the
cask at his side emptied, he threw himself on the
straw-covered floor and was instantly asleep.

At the first sign of dawn, Richard arose from his
pallet and tried to awaken the snoring musician. But

it was of no use, and off to the highway he took himself with his sleepy companion.

The journey over the mountain was frightening enough, with very few inns for shelter. Wild animals were everywhere, prowling for food, their eyes shining like hot coals from the darkness. The savage howling sent shivers up and down their spines as the boys sped over the trails as fast as darkness would allow.

"A good thing the madman gave us groschen for food," declared Richard, his teeth chattering, "or we'd have been good eating for the fierce creatures yonder."

At last, badly sunburned and with great blisters on his feet, Richard hobbled to his mother's door, so spent with weariness that he could speak only in a whisper.

"Oh, my son! What a terrible state!" Mother Hannah gasped in alarm and helped him to a cot in a darkened room. "We must work with all speed to try to cure the dreadful burns."

At last the suffering grew less and less, until Richard was well enough to explore the beautiful city with its harps and chapels and little flowered shrines.

Well content with his adventure, he rode happily back to Dresden and from its hiding place took out his play.

He must work on it at once! Then there was only one thing to do. He must give up his lessons at the Kreuz School and find himself a little place where he would not be disturbed.

Before many days he was settled in a tiny attic room at the top of an old house, and looked around his small kingdom with a happy smile. Now he could work whenever he chose, even all night long if he wished.

He hugged his pet and a glow of pride swept over him.

"Oh, Bones, what a fine castle we have, just you and I!"

A castle it was to him, with only a table and stove and tumble-down cot with shaky legs for a bed.

Day after day through the long months he scribbled away, as happy as a king in his crowded quarters, with hail and snow whirling down the slanting roof over his head.

"My play will soon be finished, old scraggle hide," he declared one morning, leaning down to pull the ears of the head resting on his foot. "One day your master will be known far and wide, and his works will be played in the greatest theatres of the land!"

The words were scarcely out of his mouth when the door opened suddenly and there stood his sister Rosalie.

"Richard! I have been searching everywhere for you," she exclaimed, looking around the poor quarters in dismay. "Mother has heard of your make-shift living, and orders you to Leipzig at once!"

Journeying again—and to be at home after a long year away! Richard sighed happily at the thought and leaped to his feet.

"Leipzig!" he cried. "Oh, Rosalie, let us start at once!"

It was not long before they arrived at the coach, arms laden.

"Step in quickly, lady. Spry there, young man. Wind's about to bring a fresh dash of snow, like as not."

Richard helped the driver to load the bulky satchel, and they were ready to begin the frosty journey to Leipzig.

"All cozy and snug as ten cats in a rug," chanted the stout old man. Puffing and wheezing, he wound a faded woolen scarf around his head and climbed up to the reins.

As quick as a wink Richard cautiously opened the door.

"Bones! Here, boy!" he whispered.

With a bound the happy pet was inside the coach, sending a shower of crystal ice over the annoyed passengers.

"Take him away! Take that animal away!" cried a woman, angrily brushing the frozen pellets from her fine new bonnet.

At the commotion the driver was back, shaking a warning finger at Richard.

"No dogs allowed—by law!" he called sharply. "Out with the beast. Out, I say!"

As he opened the door, Richard sprang to his feet, his cheeks paling.

"You would turn a poor animal out to die?" he cried. "He hasn't anyone in the whole world but me. If he can't ride, I'll have to walk all the way to Leipzig with him!"

The driver looked into the fiery eyes of his young passenger and shook his head.

"Beats me, the love of a man for his pet," he mused, half to himself. The next moment he was brusquely waving an arm. "Now look here, stranger —if you want that dog along, he'll have to ride out-side, and you with him, to see that he behaves."

"Oh, thank you, sir!"

In a few moments all three were high on the driver's box, the crusty old man looking straight ahead as he guided the horses over the rutted roads.

How good it was to be at home with his dear ones again, and to visit with Uncle Adolph in his dim, vast library that he remembered so well when he had arrived from little Eisleben.

"A happy surprise for you today, Dicker." The warm, mellow voice made his heart glad. "It is time, now, to give you this whole shelf of books, left to you by your own dear father."

He paused, letting his hands run gently over the volumes.

"Ah, Dicker, no finer gift has ever been given to man than good books to live by. The whole world is here, lad. Now we will see how much you can learn from this splendid collection."

Richard set to work at once, drinking in the great plays and poems and mighty adventures of the writers until far into the night.

Best of all were the long walks with Uncle Adolph in the calm of evening. On and on they tramped together in the peaceful dusk, speaking rapidly of the treasures they had found in books.

"It is good to talk with you, boy, for already you think like a man. Great things I expect of you someday, Richard."

The months slipped by happily until early one morning.

"My son, again I must be away with your sisters in another city," announced Mother Hannah, putting the steaming porridge on the table. "But now you are quite old enough to look after yourself. Above all, do not neglect your lessons with the masters at the Nicholas School."

And work diligently Richard did, until one blustery winter's evening, the greatest in his life.

"Bones, what do you think of a fine celebration tonight?" He looked down into the warm brown eyes. "A big concert at the Gewandhaus, and time we were on our way."

He was off through the streets whistling a jolly tune, the happy pet at his side, and soon arrived at the large building.

"You'll just have to wait outside in the passage-way, boy," he commanded, and quickly found a place in the auditorium as the orchestra members filed onto the stage.

"Beethoven Symphony." Richard read the words on the program as the lights were dimming. A hush fell over the audience and the conductor raised his arms to direct the music.

Richard sat up, electrified, as the waves of melody passed over him. Never had he heard such music before, with power that seemed to take him far into another world. Tingling chills ran up and down his back, and the quiet passages, so full of tenderness, made the tears fill his eyes to overflowing.

In a burst of triumph the music came to an end and he sat on, lost in wonder until a commanding voice broke harshly into his dreaming.

"Lights out! Time to go home, young man."

Richard looked around, startled. He was alone in the shadowy hall. Stumbling to the door, he felt a shaggy presence at his side and went out into the frosty night.

Through the streets he wandered, scarcely knowing where his footsteps led him, the mighty music of the master thundering on in his mind.

Rounding a corner, he came upon a music store and stopped to feast his eyes on the pictures of Beethoven, who had just gone to heaven. How terrible had been his suffering when he had become deaf and could no longer hear his own music.

Suddenly Richard looked up into the heavens, lighted with a crystal sweep of stars. A thrill of joy raced through him, and his jubilant cry rang out into the vast dome over his head.

"Now I know! I am going to be a great composer, like Beethoven!" His arm went around the neck of his friend. "Oh, Bones! Bones! What a wonderful night for us, boy!"

There was not a moment to lose. He would begin at once by setting his own play to music, and early the next morning he was speeding back to the store.

"Please, sir, could you give me a book that will tell me how to compose quickly?"

The clerk turned to him with a smile.

"Quickly? Takes a lifetime to compose music, young man."

"Oh, but I haven't that much time! I must do it at once!"

The bald little man shrugged his shoulders.

"Very well. Try this, and good luck to you."

The treasured book under his arm, Richard was soon back at his small table, and for seven days and nights studied the harmony book with all his might.

At last he closed it with a sigh. Now for the melodies that sang in his mind. But try as he would, he could not set down the notes.

Perhaps the horn player in the orchestra could help him. It would do no harm to ask. Scrambling into his coat, he took himself off and in a short time arrived at a tall green door with a sign in faded letters at the top.

"So you want to be a composer, hm-m-m?" Herr

Müller stood with his broad back to the meager fire, searching the bright, questioning face. "It takes a deal of patient study, young Wagner, and we begin with simple rules and exercises."

Rules, rules, rules! With heavy heart Richard buttoned his coat after the long lesson.

"You won't tell anyone that I have been here, Herr Müller?" he asked anxiously. "No one must know until I am a great composer."

The stocky horn player winked a large brown eye.

"The secret is between you and me, Wagner." The great hand shook the smaller one solemnly and Richard hurried home.

Through the weeks the lessons went on, but with all the rule learning, he still could not set his play to music. Earlier than usual one morning, he hastened back to the dingy green door.

"I am afraid the lessons are not helping me enough, sir," he began haltingly. "Perhaps later—"

His teacher nodded with a sigh of relief and stroked the scrawny gray cat under his arm.

"Ah yes, yes, Wagner. And another kind of work might be better for you than trying to become a musician."

Richard flew down the street, his heart strangely light. Suddenly he paused as an idea stole into his mind. Why had he not thought of it before?

Straight to the music store he took himself to borrow precious compositions of Beethoven, and racing home, pored over the sonata for the piano and an overture for orchestra.

This was the way to learn! Mozart's music he would study, too, and the works of other great composers, to see how they put down their melodies.

Soon he was copying the compositions so that they could be his own. Long and endless miles he walked, even to other cities to borrow the works of the masters, and from morning until night carefully and neatly put each note where it belonged on the costly music paper.

When the last composition had been returned, his heart sang for joy.

"Now I can put down my own melodies!" he cried, and like a starving man began to write, the notes falling thick and fast onto the staff.

Not once did he stop until his sonata for piano had been set down. With a deep sigh of relief, he sat looking at the long sheets before him.

"Oh Bones—think of it! Your master is making real music at last!" he cried, patting the great head on his knee.

At that very moment the door opened and in came Mother Hannah from her journey, an angry flush reddening her cheeks.

"Richard! The masters say that you have not been at the school for six whole months!" she exclaimed, loosening her bonnet. "Tonight we must have a family council to decide what is to be done with such disobedience!"

That evening all members sat in a solemn circle, eyes fixed sternly on the runaway from school. When

he could bear the silence no longer, Richard sprang to his feet.

"You see—there wasn't enough time for music!" he explained earnestly. "I am going to be like Beethoven, and write great compositions, like the master!"

Mother Hannah smoothed her apron and answered quietly.

"But a real musician plays an instrument. Beethoven performed very well, even as a small boy," said she. "Why do you not try the violin?"

Richard looked up hopefully. This was a good idea! It would help him to write for instruments with strings.

In a few days he was at work with Master Sipp,

drawing the bow across the strings of the shiny new violin, under the watchful eye of Mother Hannah. His arms ached, and often he stopped to gaze far over the chimney pots of Leipzig, brown and lazy in the pale sunlight.

Ah, there was that lovely melody again, singing joyously in his mind. If only he had a bit of paper to set it down before it flew away!

"Richard!"

Yes, yes—the violin. On scratched the bow over the strings, ending in a horrible note. For months the practicing went on, the poor family groaning at the terrible squeaks and wailing sounds.

Even Master Sipp could bear it no longer and went in search of Mother Hannah.

"I am sorry, madam, but your son will never be a violinist," he declared with a sigh. "Of all my pupils he is the worst, because his heart is not content. It is better to give up the lessons."

With a shout of joy Richard pushed the instrument into a small, dark closet, never to touch it again.

One snowy afternoon, after the school was finished for the day, he put down his pen with a smile.

"Cäcilie!" he called. "Come and listen to the finest composition ever to come from the mind of your brother!"

He flew to the piano to sing loudly and bang out parts of the new work, while his sister bent over his shoulder with puzzled frown.

"What is it, Dicker? Who will play it?" she asked.

He wheeled around to face her, hands in air.

"What is it!" he cried. "Can't you tell that it is an overture, to be played by the whole orchestra? And just think—Herr Dorn, the noted conductor, has promised to have it performed in the music hall!"

"Oh, Dicker!" Cäcilie's cry of wonder made his heart leap for joy.

The two joined hands and danced until the floor shook under their feet and the furniture went flying

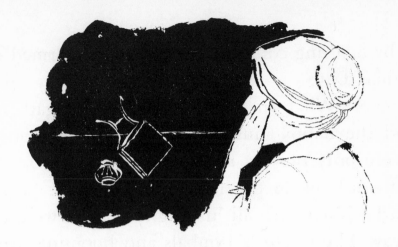

about the room. At the fearful din, Mother Hannah
ran to the scene.

"Stop! Stop!" she commanded. "The house is
tumbling down!"

Richard laughed gaily at her look of dismay and
pointed to the long sheets of notes on the piano.

"Behold, the work of a great musician!" he cried.
"And look, Mother, the parts are written in red,
green and black ink, to tell that each melody came
from magical worlds, straight to my mind!"

Mother Hannah smiled in amusement as she put
the chairs back in place.

"Better keep this world in order for the present,
my son," said she.

To the astonishment of everyone, the announce-
ment went through the city of Leipzig that a new

work by a young composer would be performed on Christmas Day.

"Dicker! What an honor!" The family gathered around the happy music maker. "And we thought you were only playing at composing!"

But once inside the hall and the music begun, Richard wished with all his might that he were far, far away. The crashing cymbals and booming drum drowned out the melody.

"Why, oh why did I make them so loud!" he mourned bitterly.

The people around him were shaking with laughter and holding their ears to shut out the noise.

Poor Richard. For long days his heart was heavy within him. There was no doubt of it. He must go to the finest teacher in all Leipzig to learn more about the writing of music.

Straight to Herr Weinlig he took himself one afternoon. There he was in long black cloak, in the very church of St. Thomas where the great Sebastian Bach had played the organ before him.

"So you are the young man whose overture has just been performed," said the master gently. "Do not feel too badly, Wagner. There must have been much good in it, or Herr Dorn would not have conducted it."

He looked carefully at the young music maker before him. Would he be content to start at the very beginning with simple exercises, he wondered.

Suddenly a bright smile lighted the kind face of the great teacher as he strode about the room. He would play a little game with the proud student.

"See, Wagner—here is a short melody that you and I will each make into a little piece of music, called a fugue. I will look at yours when it is finished, and you will look at mine, and we will decide who has made the better composition."

"A contest!" Richard chuckled at the idea. "Agreed!" he exclaimed heartily, and shaking hands with the master, he was off with a bound to work out the problem.

For months the game went on, each time Richard learning much from the great teacher. Ever more difficult the exercises became, and harder than ever the young pupil worked to please the kind master.

One morning, at the end of six long months, Herr Weinlig arose from his chair and put his hands on the shoulders of his fiery young student.

"I have no more to teach you, Wagner," said he. "A great work you have accomplished, and I am very proud indeed. Now you are ready to stand on your own feet and compose whatever you wish. Good luck to you, my dear pupil!"

The words were high praise, and his heart singing for joy, Richard began again to set down his own compositions: a polonaise, a sonata, and other works for the piano. And best of all, off they went to be printed so that everyone might play them.

But still he was not satisfied. More than anything else, he must write operas—his own stories set to music—that would be sung and acted, with costumes and scenery, to the accompaniment of an orchestra.

And that is just what Richard Wagner did. Never

did he stop writing music, no matter in what country he lived. Many were the difficulties ahead, and times without number when there was not even a crust of bread to stay his hunger.

But at last the dream of his life came true when a splendid opera house was built in lovely Bayreuth, carefully planned by the master himself.

Here Richard Wagner's great operas were performed, to the keenest delight of everyone who sat to hear them:

*The Flying Dutchman*
*Lohengrin*
*The Mastersingers of Nürnberg*
*Rienzi*
*Tristan and Isolde*
*Tannhauser*
*Parsifal*
*The Ring of the Nibelung*

Today people from the whole wide world journey to the festival in beautiful Bayreuth, and walk to the hilltop to listen, entranced, to the mighty operas of one of the greatest masters of music, Wilhelm Richard Wagner.

One piece of music from his opera, *Lohengrin*, you may already know very well. It is this stately wedding march.

## WEDDING MARCH